WHY THIS IS AN EASY READER

- This story has been carefully written to keep the young reader's interest high.

- It is told in a simple, open style, with a strong rhythm that adds enjoyment both to reading aloud and silent reading.

- There is a very high percentage of words repeated. It is this skillful repetition which helps the child to read independently. Seeing words again and again, he "practices" the vocabulary he knows, and learns with ease the words that are new.

- Only 127 different words have been used, with plurals and root words counted once.

  Over one-third of the words in this story have been used at least three times.

  Some words have been used from 19 to 38 times.

ABOUT THIS STORY

- This story is rich in concepts like *round* and *square*. Simply and exuberantly, it shows the basic *line* in drawing. It is told from the viewpoint of a zestful young artist who is having a very good time, and it will encourage young readers to see what fun they can have with a line, too.

I MADE
A LINE

Story and Pictures by
LEONARD KESSLER

Editorial Consultant:
LILIAN MOORE

WONDER BOOKS
1107 BROADWAY, NEW YORK 10, N. Y.

Introduction

These books are meant to help the young reader discover what a delightful experience reading can be. The stories are such fun that they urge the child to try his new reading skills. They are so easy to read that they will encourage and strengthen him as a reader.

The adult will notice that the sentences aren't too long, the words aren't too hard, and the skillful repetition is like a helping hand. What the child will feel is: "This is a good story—and I can read it myself!"

For some children, the best way to meet these stories may be to hear them read aloud at first. Others, who are better prepared to read on their own, may need a little help in the beginning—help that is best given freely. Youngsters who have more experience in reading alone—whether in first or second or third grade—will have the immediate joy of reading "all by myself."

These books have been planned to help all young readers grow—in their pleasure in books and in their power to read them.

Lilian Moore
Specialist in Reading
Formerly of Division of Instructional Research,
New York City Board of Education

LOOK,

a pencil!

It writes just fine.

What can I make?

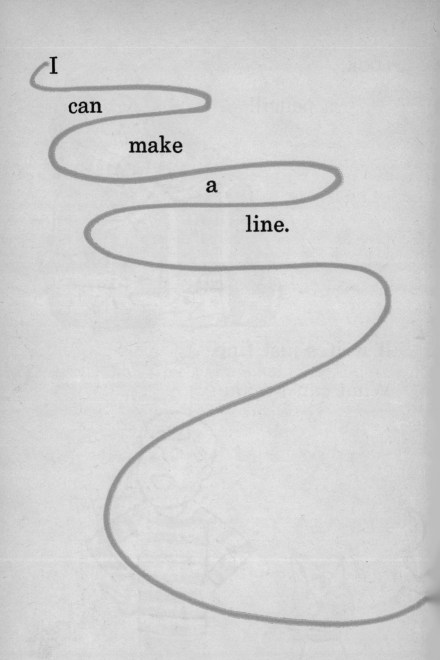

I

can

make

a

line.

I can make a line
go round and round—
Round into a circle,
See!

I can make a line
go round and round

like the sun,

or a wheel,

or a speeding train,

or an automobile.

I can make a line
go here

and there,

and here

and there.

Look—a square!

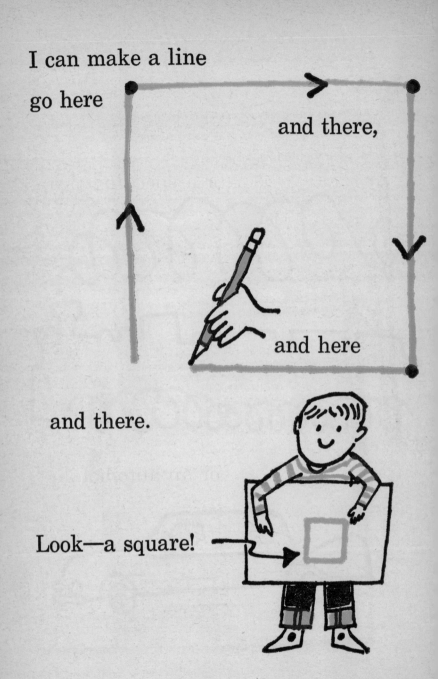

14

Like a table

or a chair.

I can make a line go up

and then down,

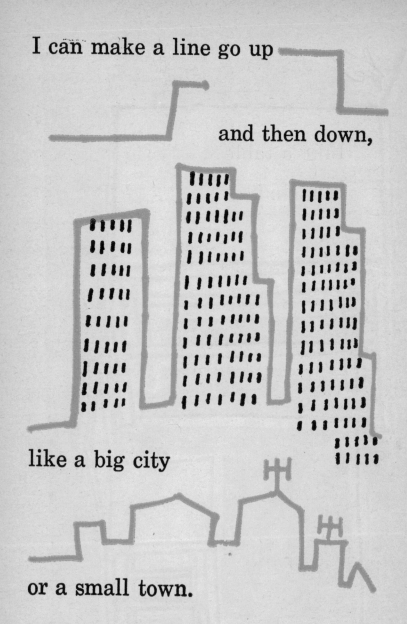

like a big city

or a small town.

Up,

Up,

Up,
like steps.

Down,

Down,

Down,
like steps.

17

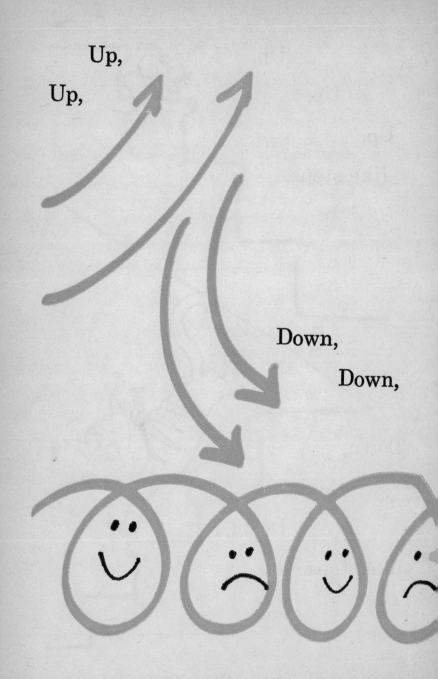

Up,

Up,

Down,

Down,

Down and up,

    like a smile.

Up and down,

    like a frown.

Up and down and
round and round.

Round and round,

and round and square.

Here and there—

I make my line

go

ANYWHERE!

I can make a line
go dash,

　　　dash,

　　　　dash,

into the sea.

I can make a line
of dots.

Lots and lots and
lots of dots—
like measles,
or marbles,
or spots on a bee.

Buzz, little bee,

but don't bite me!

I can make
just
one
small
dot,

like the eye
on a fly
on a frog
on a log.

27

Shall my line

stop

   or go—

go

   or stop?

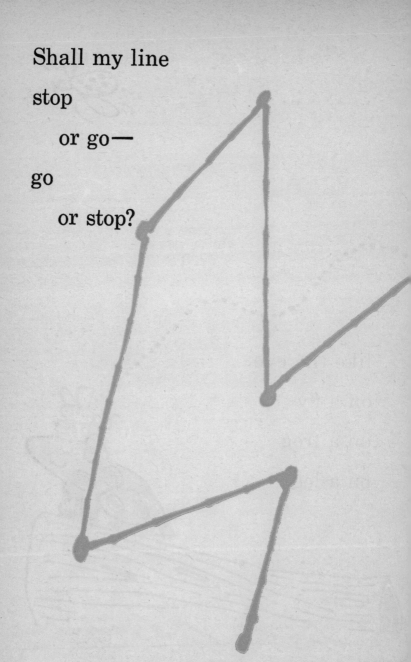

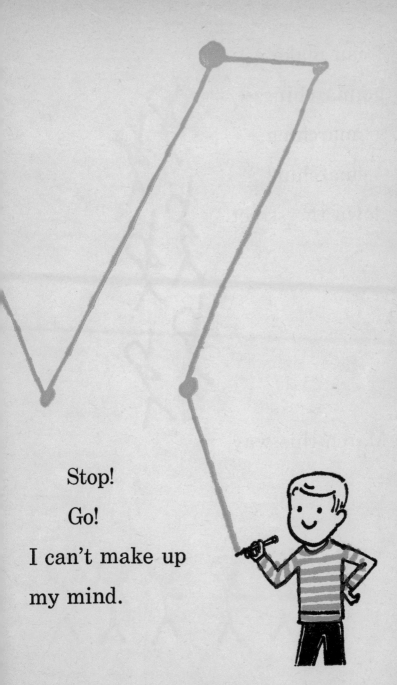

Stop!

Go!

I can't make up
my mind.

29

I can make a line
go marching —
    marching,
    marching,
down the street.

March this way,

or march that way.

About face!

STAND

STILL!

I can make a line
rock,

rock,

rock,

like a rocking chair

or a boat at sea.

Or make it go

hop,

    hop,

        hop,

and then

go . . . . .

POP!

JACK
in the
BOX

Now my line

goes

    creep,

        creep,

            creep,

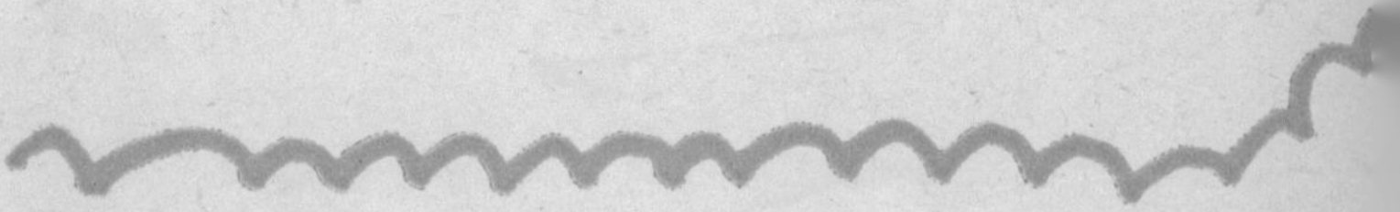

like a big fat bug

creeping on a rug

all around,

      slow,

         slow,

           slow.

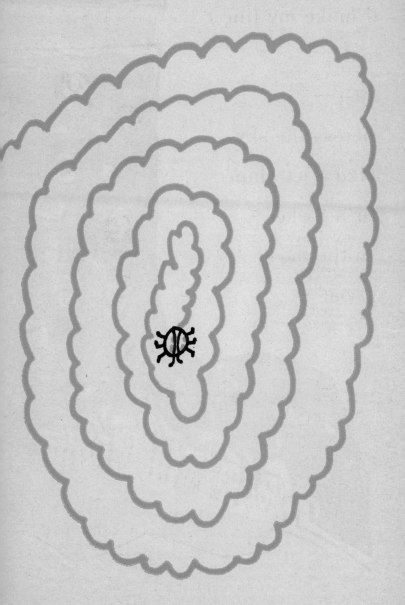

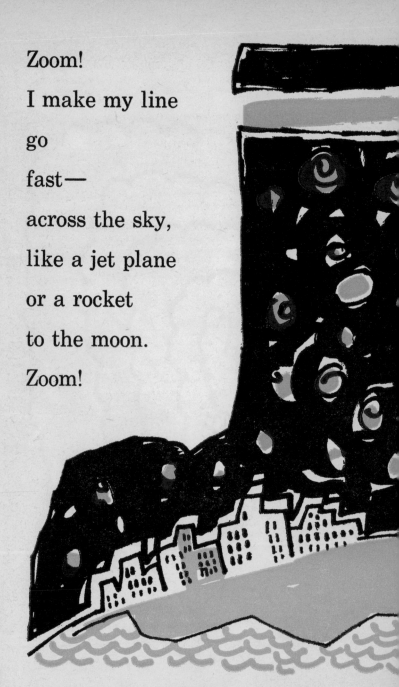

Zoom!
I make my line
go
fast—
across the sky,
like a jet plane
or a rocket
to the moon.
Zoom!

41

Fast.

Slow.

In.

Out.

Round and round

and round

about.

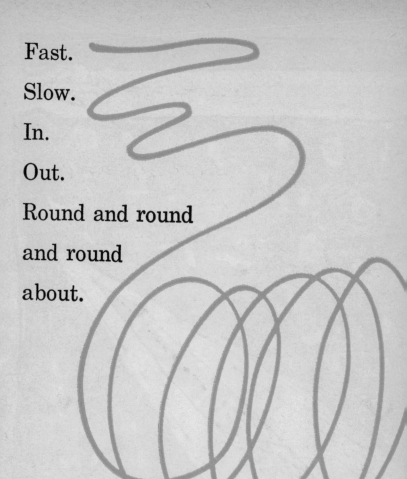

This poor little
cat can't get out!

43

I think I will make

my line

go on

and on

and on

and then

go . . . .

45

46

47

Look at all the things
I can do with a line.

I can make it thin,
I can make it fat.

I can
make it do this.

I can
make it do that.

I can make a funny cat.

I can make it rain today.

And then make all

the rain go away,

so I can play.

I can make the mouse
that lives in my house.

Look out, little mouse.

Here comes

   that cat!

I can make flowers.

I can make trees.

I can make snow.

I can make things freeze.

I can make 1 2 3

and A B C.

I can make all these things
with a line!

Now here's a line.

Let's see.

What will it be?

58

Round and square,

here and there.

Round and round

and everywhere.

What a surprise!

It
looks
like
ME!

61